super juicer

super juicer

a collection of health-enhancing juices that replenish, restore and revitalize

Christine France

Love Food ® is an imprint of Parragon Books Ltd

Parragon
Queen Street House
4 Queen Street
Bath BA1 IHE, UK

Copyright © Parragon Books Ltd 2007

Love Food ® and the accompanying heart device is a trade mark of Parragon Books Ltd

Written by Christine France
Edited by Fiona Biggs
Internal design by Talking Design
Photography by Clive Streeter
Additional photography by Günter Beer
Food Styling by Angela Drake

ISBN 978-1-4075-2322-4

Printed in China

NOTES FOR THE READER
This book uses metric and imperial measurements. Follow the same units of measurement throughout; do not mix metric and imperial. All spoon measurements are level, unless otherwise stated: teaspoons are assumed to be 5ml and tablespoons are assumed to be 15ml. Unless otherwise stated, milk is assumed to be whole, eggs and individual fruits such as bananas are medium, and pepper is freshly ground black pepper.

- Recipes using raw or very lightly cooked eggs should be avoided by children, the elderly, pregnant women, convalescents and anyone suffering from an illness.
- Sufferers from nut allergies should be aware that some of the ready-made ingredients in the recipes in this book may contain nuts. Pregnant and breast-feeding women are advised to avoid eating peanuts and peanut products.

contents

introduction

If you're new to juicing, then you have a real treat in store. Not only are the health benefits of freshly extracted juices unbelievably good, but you'll be surprised how wonderful the flavours can be. Even foods you never believed you would enjoy are suddenly transformed into succulent, rich-tasting super juices in a matter of seconds.

Juicing Equipment

There are basically three types of juicer: centrifugal, masticating and press. The majority of modern domestic juicers work on the centrifugal force method — the fruit is ground against blades to break it up, while spinning at high speed to force out the juice through a fine mesh. This is the type we have designed the recipes in this book for. It's as simple as popping in the fruit or vegetables, switching on and catching the juice that comes out in a matter of seconds.

Purchasing Pointers

- It's worth buying the best quality juicer you can afford, particularly if you plan to juice often or in large amounts. As always, you get what you pay for and what price can you put on good health?
- A compact, well-designed machine takes up as little space as possible on your worktop and looks good, too.
- A powerful motor is essential to make juices efficiently and quickly.
- Check noise levels, as juicers vary and some can be very loud — if you plan to juice early in the morning, it could be a rather sharp wake-up!
- Variable speed is useful if you are juicing a variety of different ingredients — for example high speed for apples and carrots, low speed for mangoes and grapes.
- Ensure the juicer is easy to clean, with simple, unfussy parts that come apart easily.
- Check that the juicer has non-slip feet to keep it in place on the worktop.
- Most juicers now have a safety-lock lid, and it's worth testing this before buying.

Additional Kit

- Hand-held blender — turns juices into smoothies; some ingredients such as bananas or avocados are not suitable for juicing but do add very valuable fibre and nutrients. A free-standing, jug-type blender also makes smoothies, but is more bulky.
- Measuring jugs — most juicers provide one, but you may find a spare one useful too.
- Small whisk — for combining juices that tend to settle and separate quickly.

- Sharp knives – if produce has to be cut, use the sharpest knife possible to avoid unnecessary vitamin loss.

Advantages of Home Juicing

So, why don't we just buy ready-made juices from the supermarket? Well, there's nothing wrong with shop-bought juices, it's just that there's really no comparison – home-made juices are better in so many ways:

- Unless you buy freshly-made juice from a juice bar, shop-bought juices will have lost valuable nutrients during storage. Juices made at home can be absolutely fresh and consumed immediately, retaining maximum amounts of nutrients, and more flavour.
- Shop-bought juices have usually been heat-treated or have additives to help them keep longer. Fruit 'drinks' are not entirely made from juice – they can be made from concentrates mixed with water.
- If you make your own juices, you're not buying expensive and wasteful packaging.

- Juicing at home need not be expensive if you buy ingredients when they're in season and look for bargains in your local shops.
- Home juicing is fun – you can create different combinations that will never be available in the shops. Experiment and make your own concoctions to suit your own taste, or to help a particular health condition.

...and the Disadvantages?

- Juicers can be bulky, so make sure you have enough space in your kitchen to keep your juicer out on the worktop all the time; it's unlikely that it will be used regularly if it's stored in a cupboard – out of sight is out of mind!
- Even well-designed juicers are not easy to wash up. The filter should never be allowed to dry with food deposits on it. Just pop it into a bowl of hot soapy water before the pulp dries, and the rest is relatively easy. Most parts can be put in the dishwasher (although you should consult the manufacturer's handbook before doing this).

Uses for Pulp

The pulp left behind after juicing still contains valuable fibre and nutrients, so you shouldn't waste it:

- Add to cakes and bakes – for example carrot cake, fruit cake, biscuits and muffins.
- Stir into soups and casseroles to thicken, or add to minced meat mixtures for burgers or Bolognese sauce.
- Add to the compost heap – as pulp is already partially broken down it accelerates the composting process.

Nutritional Benefits of Juicing

We all know that we should be eating a minimum of five portions of fruit and vegetables each day, but it's not always easy. Juicing is just one more way to get your fruit and vegetable counts up, and add life-enhancing nutrients to your diet in an easily absorbed form. Regular juicing helps increase vitality, boost energy levels and fight disease.

Just 150 ml/5 fl oz of juice counts as one of your five-a-day portions, but remember that juice cannot count for more than one portion as it does not contain all the nutrients you get from whole fruit and vegetables.

The fibre in fruit and vegetables contains beneficial nutrients – because juicing breaks up these fibres, it allows them to be available to the body in an easily digestible form. The enzymes released actually help the body to absorb vital vitamins and minerals.

Basic Nutrition

No single food can provide all the nutrition we need to stay healthy, so you should aim to eat a wide variety of different foods to obtain all the necessary nutrients.

• Carbohydrate

Carbohydrate is a form of fuel, which the body uses to make energy. There are basically two types of carbohydrate: fast-release or 'simple' carbohydrates, and slow-release, 'complex' or starchy carbohydrates.

Simple carbohydrates, found in sugar and honey, should be eaten only in limited amounts as excessive quantities can cause health problems such as diabetes, obesity, heart disease and cancer. Complex carbohydrates, found mainly in whole grains, pulses, vegetables and fruits, should make up about two thirds of your diet.

• **Fat**

The body uses fats to make energy. There are two main types: saturated fat, usually solid at room temperature, is mainly found in meat and dairy products and processed foods. A diet rich in saturated fat can lead to heart disease and obesity.

Unsaturated fats are usually liquid at room temperature. These are polyunsaturated, including the Omega 3 and Omega 6 oils found in oily fish, nuts and seeds, and monounsaturated, found in olive oil and rapeseed oil. These essential oils are linked to healthy brain function, reduced risk of heart disease and lower cholesterol levels.

It's recommended that around two thirds of our fat intake should be polyunsaturated and no more than a third should be saturated.

• **Protein**

Our bodies need protein for growth and cell repair. The main sources are meat, fish, eggs and soya beans, which contain all the amino acids we need. Vegetables, particularly pulses, are also a good source if you eat a wide variety, and these contribute complex carbohydrates, which meat sources don't have, to the diet.

Most of us eat too much protein – for instance, an adult female needs just 45 g/1¹/₂ oz per day, and an adult male just 55 g/2 oz per day.

• **Fibre**

Although we cannot digest fibre, it is essential for keeping the bowels healthy and allows other nutrients to be absorbed.

Fibre is divided into two groups, soluble and insoluble, both found in wholegrain cereals, pulses, fruits and vegetables. Soluble fibre can help to reduce levels of cholesterol in the blood and regulate blood sugar levels. Insoluble fibre helps prevent constipation and may prevent bowel cancer.

Healthy eating guidelines recommend that we should eat around 18 g/³/₄ oz of fibre per day.

• **Vitamins**

Vitamins are organic substances that are essential for general good health and tissue repair, and also help the body to release the energy from carbohydrates. Each vitamin has specific uses in the body – vitamin A, for instance, is needed for healthy growth, good skin and vision and a healthy immune system.

Some vitamins can be stored in the body (A, D, E, K and B_{12}) but others must be consumed regularly to maintain healthy levels. Water-soluble vitamins (B complex and C) are easily destroyed during processing, storage and cooking. Fat-soluble vitamins (A, D, E and K) are more stable.

Juicing is a good way to make sure we consume a wide variety of vitamin-rich foods every day.

• **Minerals**

Minerals are inorganic substances that perform many functions in keeping our bodies healthy. Only about 20 minerals are thought to be essential and need to be obtained from foods.

Some minerals, such as potassium, which helps maintain healthy nerves, blood pressure and fluid levels in the body, are needed in relatively large amounts. Others, such as selenium, a powerful antioxidant which can protect against heart disease, are needed in such small quantities that they are known as 'trace elements'.

Super Foods

All foods have some nutritional value, but some foods are more nutrient-packed than others. Here are some of the very best foods to include in your juice drinks:

Apples – rich in antioxidants, vitamin C for healthy skin and soluble fibre to reduce blood cholesterol. Contain quercetin, a phytonutrient that may help fight cancer.

Avocados – very energy-rich, and a good source of vitamin E, which repairs tissues, lowers blood pressure and reduces cholesterol. Use in smoothies.

Bananas – very energy-rich, high in fibre and a good source of potassium, which regulates blood pressure. Use in smoothies.

Beetroot – rich in potassium, iron and folic acid, so good for the blood and arteries. The leafy tops are rich in beta-carotene, an antioxidant that the body converts to vitamin A.

Blueberries – the top antioxidant fruit boosts the immune system, helps fight conditions associated with ageing, such as Alzheimer's disease, protects eyesight and destroys free radicals linked with cancer.

Broccoli – rich in cancer-fighting phytochemicals, with vitamins A and C, folic acid, which helps prevent birth defects, and potassium, which helps regulate blood pressure.

Ginger – a natural antibiotic that helps digestion and stimulates the circulation.

Nuts and seeds – a great source of protein and the essential oils, Omega 3 and 6, plus protein, vitamins and minerals. Linseeds are rich in phytoestrogens, which can regulate female hormones.

Onions and garlic – the allium family has anti-bacterial and anti-fungal compounds, and phytochemicals which fight cancer and heart disease and help the liver eliminate toxins from the body.

Oranges – a good source of vitamins A, C, B$_6$, beta-carotene and folic acid. Citrus fruits are high in lutein, a carotenoid that helps reduce the risk of colon cancer.

Soya – milk and yogurt are rich in powerful isoflavones, which fight cancer, reduce cholesterol and relieve menopausal symptoms.

Spinach – dark green leafy vegetables are rich in B vitamins, particularly folates, essential for normal tissue growth, and are particularly useful during pregnancy. Spinach contains more protein than most vegetables.

Tomatoes – a great source of lycopene, a phytochemical that has cancer-fighting properties and helps protect against heart disease. One large tomato provides 40 per cent of our daily requirement of vitamin C.

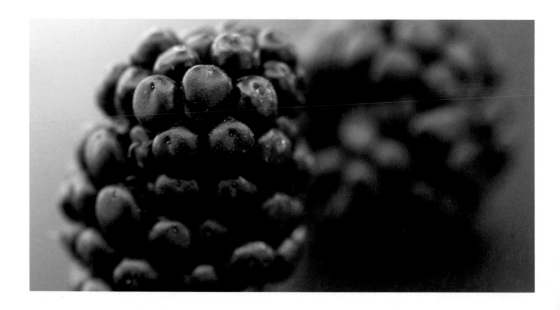

Preparing for Juicing

Buying the right produce and storing and preparing it well is critical to the amount of juicy nutrients you'll get:

- Use organic produce if possible, then you can use the whole fruit or vegetable without worrying about pesticide and herbicide residues.
- Always wash fresh produce, scrubbing with a soft brush if necessary. If not organic, wash in water with a little washing-up liquid, then rinse thoroughly.
- To get maximum nutritive value from fresh produce, it's best to juice ingredients whole. Most modern juicers have large feed tubes to allow for this. So, unless it's necessary to chop items to get them into the juicer, leave them whole with skins, cores and all. Bitter or waxy peel and large stones should be removed to avoid damaging the juicer.
- Use really fresh produce that's at its peak, and don't be tempted to buy bruised or damaged over-ripe fruit and vegetables, which will have lost food value and flavour.
- Store most vegetables in a cool, airy place, and salads in the crisper compartment of the refrigerator, but use them all quickly before nutrients are lost. Soft, berry-type fruits can be stored in the refrigerator but need to be used quickly for maximum food value. Fruits such as apples, pears, tropical and citrus fruits are best stored at cool room temperature as they give up more juice that way.
- Wash produce before storage, if possible, so that it's ready for juicing at any time.

Juicing for Children

- Juices are a great way to encourage fussy eaters. Children often find the idea of colourful juices more exciting than a plate of vegetables. In addition, it's easy to sneak in a carrot when you're juicing oranges.
- Adding an apple or pear to a vegetable juice can make it more palatable for children.
- Juices should be diluted for children, with still or sparkling mineral water or lemonade.
- Young children love to watch juices being made and often enjoy helping to prepare, but for safety's sake don't allow them to use the juicer themselves.

- Do make sure that children (and adults, too!) brush their teeth after drinking fresh juices, as even natural sugars can cause tooth decay.

Does Juicing Cost a Fortune?

The short answer is no, as long as you shop sensibly:

- Use produce that's at the peak of its season, when it's not only cheaper but also has the finest flavour and maximum nutrients.
- Look out for special offers and bulk-buys in fruit and vegetables. Many greengrocers will sell a whole tray or box of produce for a cheaper price.
- Avoid over-packaged produce and buy loose if possible, which is cheaper and more environmentally friendly.
- Combine some of your purchasing with a friend or neighbour who also has a juicer, to bulk buy and save money.
- If you buy more produce than you need at one time, freeze some for later, or make a larger batch of juice and freeze that for later use, in portion-sized amounts for easy thawing.
- Be creative with your juicing. Just check out the fridge or fruit bowl and have a go – you'll soon find that there's no need for anything to go to waste.
- When you have a glut in the vegetable garden, it's time to start juicing; make the most of home-grown produce as it's cheaper and more organic than buying.

Safety Notes

- If you are taking medication, consult your doctor before consuming grapefruit juice, as this can inhibit some medications.
- If you're adding supplements or herbal additives, for example spirulina or ginseng, read the manufacturer's instructions for dosage, and, if in doubt, check with your doctor.
- If you're new to juicing, start with no more than two juices per day, to give your body a chance to adjust.

vitality-boosting

The moment you wake up in the morning is the best time of day to drink fresh juice, as that's when your body is most able to absorb those wonderful vitamins and minerals. Resist the temptation to make juice the night before – you'll lose some of the goodness and there's nothing better than really fresh juice.

serves 1–2

1 ripe mango
1 orange
$^{1}/_{2}$ pomegranate

tropical sunrise

This beautifully coloured juice is packed with powerful heart-protective and cancer-fighting antioxidants, plus vitamins B and C. Mangoes, oranges and pomegranate seeds are all good sources of potassium, which helps to regulate blood pressure.

Remove the stone from the mango, and peel the orange. Juice them together and pour into glasses. Peel the pomegranate, reserve 1 tablespoon of the seeds and juice the rest. Pour into the orange and mango juice and sprinkle with the reserved pomegranate seeds.

serves 1–2

100 ml/3¹/₂ fl oz boiling
  water
1 green tea sachet,
  or 1 tsp green tea
1 carrot
1 apple
small handful flat-leaf
  parsley
sprigs of flat-leaf parsley,
  to garnish

bright eyes

The carrots and parsley in this juice are packed with carotenoids to brighten the eyes and skin and help cleanse the liver. It's also full of antioxidants, which regulate blood pressure, lower cholesterol and fight heart disease and cancer.

Pour the boiling water onto the green tea and leave to stand for 4 minutes. Strain and cool slightly. Juice the carrot, apple and parsley. Stir the juice into the tea, pour into glasses and serve warm or cold, garnished with parsley sprigs.

serves 1–2

$^1/_2$ peach
1 small apple
$^1/_2$ kiwi fruit
55 g/2 oz green grapes
200 g/7 oz honeydew
  melon flesh
slice of kiwi fruit,
  to garnish

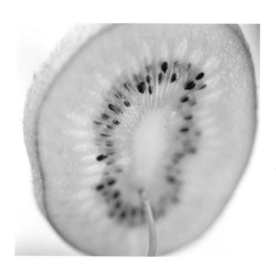

fruity refresher

Rich in vitamin C and beta-carotene, this is an excellent cleanser, diuretic and energizer to liven up a sluggish system in the mornings. Melon cleanses the intestine, bladder and kidneys and clears the skin. Grape skins contain tannins that help to stimulate the appetite.

Halve and stone the peach. Juice the peach, apple and kiwi fruit, then add the grapes and melon. Stir the juice, pour into glasses and serve, garnished with the slice of kiwi fruit.

serves 1–2

2 small beetroot
1 carrot
1 pear
$^1/_2$ lime
2.5-cm/1-inch piece of
  fresh ginger

red reviver

Beetroot is very rich in potassium, which is highly effective in keeping blood pressure low. Rich in vitamins and antioxidants, the Red Reviver protects against ageing free radicals and helps normal cell function. Ginger is a good wake-up, as it stimulates circulation and peps up the digestion.

Juice the beetroot and carrot, then juice the pear, lime and ginger. Mix together, pour into glasses and serve.

serves 1–2

1 pomegranate
$^1/_2$ small orange
4 passion fruit
100–125 ml/3$^1/_2$–4$^1/_2$ fl oz
   sparkling mineral water

passionate juice fizz

This delicate pink drink is powerfully rich in antioxidants, calcium, vitamin C and vitamin E, phytochemicals that protect the heart, and enzymes that are good for the digestive system. Mineral water speeds up the absorption of the nutrients.

Peel the rind from the pomegranate and peel the orange, leaving on the white pith. Scoop the flesh from the passion fruit. Juice the pomegranate with the orange and pulp from 3 passion fruit. Pour into a glass and stir in the remaining passion fruit pulp. Top up with the mineral water and serve.

serves 1–2

1 orange
large sprig of fresh mint
200 g/7 oz cantaloupe
   melon flesh
sprigs of mint, to
   decorate

wake-up juice

A light and refreshing drink for a fresh start after a late night, packed with vitamin C. Melon juice is diuretic and rich in healing beta-carotene. The aromatic oils in mint aid and soothe the digestion and help to calm the nerves, while at the same time freshening the breath.

Peel the orange, leaving on the white pith. Juice the orange, mint and melon. Pour into glasses and serve, decorated with sprigs of mint.

serves 1–2

1 pink grapefruit
1 orange
$^1/_2$ lemon
$^1/_2$ lime
slice of lime, to decorate

pink zinger

Packed with vitamin C, which mops up the free radicals that cause ageing, the Pink Zinger helps with healing and strengthening the body's resistance to infections. It's an energizing start to the day that flushes toxins from the intestines for clear skin and a healthy system.

Peel the grapefruit, orange, lemon and lime, leaving on the white pith. Juice the grapefruit, orange, lemon and lime together. Pour into a glass and serve with a slice of lime on the rim of the glass.

serves 1–2

1 ruby grapefruit, peeled
140 g/5 oz raspberries
55 g/2 oz cranberries

rosy glow

A vibrant ruby-coloured juice, rich in beta-carotene, antioxidants and bioflavonoids which help absorption of vitamin C. Cranberry helps with bladder problems and can cure cystitis.

Cut the grapefruit into quarters, then pack half into the juicer. Top with the raspberries and cranberries, then add the remaining grapefruit. Juice all the fruit together. Pour into glasses and serve immediately.

serves 1–2

200 g/7 oz strawberries
100 g/3^1/$_2$ oz raspberries
100 ml/3^1/$_2$ fl oz soya
 milk
40 g/1^1/$_2$ oz unsweetened
 muesli

breakfast berry smoothie

This breakfast-in-a-glass is packed with sustaining nutrients to keep up your energy levels all morning. Strawberries contain lignin, which helps reduce blood cholesterol, and oats are one of the most effective cholesterol-lowering foods.

Reserve a strawberry for decoration, then juice the remainder with the raspberries. Place the juice in a blender with the soya milk and muesli, and blend until almost smooth. Pour into glasses, top each smoothie with half a strawberry and serve.

serves 1–2

$^1/_2$ cucumber
2 apples
15 g/$^1/_2$ oz fresh
   coriander, leaves and
   stems

cucumber cooler

Cucumber is high in water content so it's great for rehydrating and refreshing the system, and is a very good diuretic. Apples contain natural sugars for an energy lift. Coriander promotes good digestion and can remove toxins. It also helps the circulation and is good for healthy eyesight.

Cut a few long strips from the cucumber and reserve. Juice the apple, coriander and cucumber together. Pour into glasses, add the cucumber strips and serve.

empowering

When energy levels dip during a busy day, it's easy to reach for a quick sugar-fix or caffeine, but what you really need is longer-lasting energy to build and repair, for brain power and renewed strength. Invest in a flask to carry your juice to work, to the gym, or anywhere your busy life takes you, ready to refuel at any time of day.

serves 1–2

2 nectarines
100 g/3^1/$_2$ oz green
  seedless grapes
100 g/3^1/$_2$ oz soya yogurt
^{1}/$_2$ tsp honey, preferably
  Manuka
1 tbsp sunflower seeds

sunshine smoothie

A vitamin-packed, energizing smoothie that's a satisfying and healthy snack at any time of day. It's rich in vitamin A, which helps maintain a healthy skin and immune system.

Halve and stone the nectarines then juice with the grapes. Add to the yogurt, honey and half the sunflower seeds and blend until smooth. Pour into a glass, sprinkle with the remaining sunflower seeds and serve.

serves 1–2

350 g/12 oz dark sweet
  cherries
$^1/_2$ lime
1 apple
100 g/3$^1/_2$ oz red grapes
40 g/1$^1/_2$ oz soya yogurt

cherry pink

Naturally sweet and energy-rich, this juice is a perfect midday boost when you're working hard. It's high in vitamin C, cancer-fighting phytochemicals, antioxidants, and calcium for strength.

Stone the cherries. Halve the lime. Juice the apple, cherries, grapes and lime together. Whisk in the yogurt, pour into glasses and serve.

serves 1–2

2 apples
1 small banana
2 tbsp bio yogurt
1 tbsp light tahini
$^1/_2$ tsp sesame seeds, for
sprinkling

banana velvet

This juice provides a good combination of natural sugars for instant energy and soluble fibre for slow-release energy, and is a good source of protein and calcium for building strong muscles and bones.

Juice the apples. Add the peeled banana, yogurt and tahini. Blend until smooth and frothy. Pour into a glass, sprinkle with sesame seeds and serve.

serves 1–2

1 small courgette
1 celery stick
40 g/1½ oz baby leaf
 spinach
40 g/1½ oz alfalfa
 sprouts
2 apples
1 tsp alfalfa sprouts,
 to garnish

rapid recharge

This is a treasure trove of B vitamins, iron, healing phytochemicals, calcium and protein, plus fruit sugars for a quick energy boost. It regulates blood pressure, reduces fluid retention, and helps to strengthen tissues and bones.

Top and tail the courgette and pack into the juicer with the celery, add the spinach and the alfalfa, then the apples. Juice all the ingredients, then pour into glasses. Garnish with a few alfalfa sprouts and serve.

serves 1–2

200 g/7 oz parsnips
100 g/3¹/₂ oz broccoli
   florets
100 g/3¹/₂ oz peas
large sprig of fresh mint
2 apples
paprika pepper,
   for sprinkling

the protector

This delicate, pale green juice is great for all-round body maintenance, as it's very high in a good range of nutrients, including vitamins A, B and C, protein and iron. It's also rich in potassium, which helps normal cell function.

Pack the parsnips, broccoli, peas, mint and apples into the juicer, then juice all the ingredients together. Pour into a glass and sprinkle with paprika pepper to serve.

serves 1–2

1 pear
40 g/1 1/2 oz young
   spinach
4 sprigs parsley
1/4 cucumber
1/2 ripe Hass avocado
1/2 tsp spirulina powder
1 brazil nut

avocado power pack

A super-smoothie, packed with antioxidants, vitamins and minerals, including B vitamins, which regulate brain and nerve function. Spirulina contains the highest concentration of nutrients in any food and helps replenish the body's vital stores.

Pack the pear, spinach, parsley and cucumber into the juicer and juice. Remove the stone and skin from the avocado and add to the juice. Blend until smooth, then pour into a glass.

Mix the spirulina powder with just enough water to make a thick liquid, then swirl into the juice. Roughly chop the brazil nut and sprinkle over to serve.

serves 1–2

2 apples
1 banana
1 tbsp peanut butter
slices of apple, to
  decorate

peanut power

This caramel-coloured smoothie has a rich, naturally sweet taste. It's a good source of energy, with protein and calcium for strength and tissue-building.

Juice the apples. Peel the banana and blend with the apple and peanut butter until smooth. Pour into glasses, decorate the rim of the glasses with apple slices and serve.

serves 1–2

$^1/_2$ sweet-fleshed
  pineapple
1 small red finger chilli
85 g/3 oz watercress
$^1/_2$ lime with skin
$^1/_2$ ripe Hass avocado
sprigs of fresh
  watercress, to garnish

green zapper

This juice is very energizing, owing to the combination of sugars. A good source of beta-carotene and folic acid for strong growth and immunity, it cleanses the liver of toxins and aids digestion. Chilli helps lower cholesterol and stimulates circulation.

Peel and quarter the pineapple. Halve the chilli and remove the seeds. Juice the pineapple together with the watercress, lime and chilli. Scoop out the avocado flesh and blend with the juice until smooth. Pour into glasses, garnish with sprigs of watercress and serve.

serves 1–2

1 orange
200 g/7 oz sweet potato
2 pears
2 brazil nuts

just a sweetie

This delicious juice is packed with nutrients, particularly vitamins A, C, B6 and folic acid. Sweet potatoes and pears are low GI for slow-release energy to keep you going through a long day.

Peel the orange, leaving some of the white pith. Juice the sweet potato, pears and orange. Pour into a glass, roughly chop the nuts and sprinkle over the top to serve.

serves 1–2

1 pear
150 g/5^1/$_2$ oz blueberries
100 g/3^1/$_2$ oz soya yogurt
^{1}/$_2$ tsp agave syrup
2 tsp toasted flaked
  almonds

blueberry nectar

Blueberries are super-rich in antioxidants and help keep your brain healthy in later life. Agave is a low-GI natural sweetener which helps keep blood sugar levels constant. Yogurt and almonds provide calcium for bone strength.

Juice the pear and blueberries. Add the yogurt and agave syrup and whisk or blend until smooth and bubbly. Pour into a glass, sprinkle with the almonds and serve.

uplifting

If it's hard to summon up the enthusiasm to enjoy life, a juicy pep-up will lift your spirits. The stress-busting ingredients can reduce blood pressure, increase energy levels and cleanse the system. These antioxidant-rich juices will help you detox, boosting your levels of feel-good hormones, revitalizing your body and clearing your mind.

serves 1–2

$^1/_2$ small pineapple
85 g/3 oz blackberries
85 g/3 oz blueberries
1 tsp goji berries, roughly
   chopped

black 'n' blue

A good detoxing drink to cleanse the intestines and clear the sinuses, a general pep-up for a run-down system. All the berries, particularly the blueberries and goji berries, are very rich in disease-fighting, antioxidants.

Cut the pineapple into chunks and juice with the blackberries and blueberries. Pour into a glass and sprinkle with the chopped goji berries to serve.

serves 1–2

2 spring onions
3 tomatoes
25 g/1 oz fresh basil
1 garlic clove
ice cubes
shredded spring onion, to
 garnish

tomato twister

A flavour-packed tomato-based juice that's a great source of beta-carotene and cancer-fighting lycopene. Basil calms the nerves and counteracts stress, and garlic is a good system cleanser and a natural antibiotic.

Trim the spring onions. Place one tomato in the juicer and firmly pack in the onions, basil and garlic, then top with the remaining tomatoes. Juice all the ingredients, then pour into glasses with ice cubes. Top with shredded spring onion and serve.

serves 1–2

¹/₂ Galia melon
3 celery sticks
125 g/4¹/₂ oz blackberries
1 kiwi fruit

the reviver

Refreshing and rehydrating, cleansing and calming, and rich in vitamin C to boost the body's resistance, this juice is a perfect reviver after a hard day at the office.

Peel the melon and cut into chunks. Pack into the juicer with 1 celery stick, the blackberries and kiwi fruit. Juice all the ingredients together, then pour into glasses and serve with the remaining celery sticks to stir.

serves 1–2

$^1/_2$ Webbs lettuce
1 large carrot
10 g/$^1/_4$ oz fresh
  coriander
3 radishes, with leaves
pepper
sprig of fresh coriander
  and some carrot sticks,
  to garnish

carrot calmer

This calming juice is a good tonic for the digestive system, eyes and skin. It's also mildly diuretic and slightly sedative. Webbs lettuce contains more natural calming substances than any other food and coriander helps to reduce cholesterol.

Cut the lettuce into chunks and pack into the juicer with the carrot, coriander and radishes. Juice together, then pour into a glass. Sprinkle with pepper and add a sprig of coriander and some carrot sticks to serve.

serves 1–2

150 ml/5 fl oz boiling
  water
1 ginseng tea bag or
  1 tsp ginseng tea
1 apple
40 g/1¹/₂ oz wild rocket
  leaves

stressbuster

A teatime juice that helps liver and kidney function and prevents fluid retention.
Ginseng is a natural stimulant that helps to combat stress and lifts the mood.

Pour the boiling water over the tea bag or tea, and leave
to stand for 4 minutes. Strain. Place the apple in the juicer
and pack the rocket leaves firmly on top, then juice. Stir
the juice into the tea, pour into glasses and serve warm or
cold.

serves 1–2

$^1/_2$ lemon
2 apples
85 g/3 oz stoned prunes
2 pears
freshly grated nutmeg

spiced fruit boost

Just the juice to give you a lift when you're flagging, it's packed with long-lasting energy, with good amounts of vitamin C and beta-carotene. Nutmeg is good for digestion, and is also an aphrodisiac!

Peel the lemon, leaving on a layer of white pith. Juice the apples, lemon, prunes and pears together. Pour into glasses, sprinkle with grated nutmeg and serve.

serves 1–2

$^1/_2$ fennel bulb, with
    leaves
1 apple
1 carrot
1 small red pepper

red pep-up

Full of disease-fighting, anti-ageing antioxidants, this drink provides lots of energy from natural sweetness and stimulants to help you get through the day.

Remove a few leaves from the fennel and reserve for garnish. Pack the fennel, apple, carrot and pepper into the juicer and juice all the ingredients together. Pour into glasses, add a sprig of fennel leaves to each and serve.

serves 1–2

6 apricots
1 orange
1 fresh lemon grass stalk
2-cm/³/₄-inch piece of
  fresh ginger

apricot buzz

If your energy levels are low after lunch, this is the one to give you renewed vigour. It's rich in natural sugars, iron, potassium and beta-carotene. Ginger speeds up the metabolic rate, lemon grass helps to relax the stomach, and both aid digestion.

Halve and stone the apricots. Peel the orange, leaving some of the white pith. Cut the lemon grass into chunks. Place the apricots, orange, lemon grass and ginger in the juicer and juice all the ingredients together. Pour into glasses and serve.

serves 1–2

2 peaches
140 g/5 oz red grapes
115 g/4 oz strawberries
1 passion fruit
seeds from ¹/₂ vanilla pod

passionate magic

A great all-rounder for the system, packed with powerful antioxidants to slow down the signs of ageing, as well as healing vitamins A and C. It also has mildly sedative, liver-cleansing and anti-arthritic properties, from the phytochemicals in the fruits.

Halve and stone the peaches and juice with the grapes and strawberries. Halve the passion fruit and scoop out the flesh, scrape the seeds from the vanilla pod and stir both into the juice. Pour into glasses and serve.

restoring

Whether you're fighting an infection or recovering
from an injury, battling with pmt or simply feeling
tired, pour yourself a healing juice. If you have
a cold, try a hot blackcurrant toddy packed with
vitamin C and honey. Cure a hangover with a quick-
fix juice to restore blood sugar levels and rehydrate
the system.

serves 1–2

$^1/_2$ sweet pineapple
2-cm/$^3/_4$-inch slice
   thin-skinned lemon
2-cm/$^3/_4$-inch piece of
   fresh ginger

tummy soother

Pineapple juice is great for improving digestion and soothing an upset tummy. The healing enzyme bromelin reduces bruising, so it can help with recovery from an injury. It's also a good source of vitamin C, which helps to heal and fight infection. Lemons are gently diuretic and help to cleanse the system.

Juice the pineapple, lemon and ginger together, then pour into glasses and serve.

serves 1–2

flesh and seeds of
 1/4 watermelon
150 g/5 1/2 oz raspberries
ice cubes

red cooler

A great hangover cure, rehydrating, cleansing and diuretic, and packed with vitamin C, which is depleted by alcohol. It also helps build the body's natural immunity, and the natural sugars will raise low blood sugar and revitalize you.

Juice the watermelon flesh with the raspberries. Pour into glasses over ice and serve.

serves 1–2

1 apple
200 g/7 oz blackcurrants
100 ml/3^1/$_2$ fl oz boiling
  water
1 tsp set honey,
  preferably Manuka

hot blackcurrant toddy

This comforting toddy is a great natural way to fight a sore throat, cold or flu.
Blackcurrants have four times the vitamin C of oranges. Manuka honey is very rich
in vitamins and minerals and has powerful anti-bacterial properties.

Juice the apple with the blackcurrants. Add the honey to
the boiling water and stir to dissolve, then stir in the juice.
Pour into a glass and serve immediately.

serves 1–2

1 kiwi fruit
1 apple
115 g/4 oz seedless
  white grapes

kiwi juice box

Sweet and energizing, this juice is packed with vitamin C. Grapes are good for restoring the body's alkaline balance and also a great cleanser, useful for detoxing and restoring healthy bowel movement.

Juice the kiwi fruit and apple, then the grapes. Pour into glasses and serve just as it is, or pour over ice.

serves 1–2

1 white grapefruit
1 orange
1 kiwi fruit
15 drops echinacea
   tincture
thinly pared twists of
   orange zest, to decorate

cold comforter

This is packed with vitamin C to fight colds and flu, with an added boost from echinacea, a powerful immune system booster that helps increase white blood cells to fight infection.

Peel the grapefruit and orange, leaving on some of the white pith. Juice the grapefruit, orange and kiwi fruit together. Stir in the echinacea drops and pour into glasses. Add a twist of orange zest to each and serve.

serves 1–2

1 orange
55 g/2 oz cranberries
1 banana
100 g/3¹/₂ oz soya yogurt
fine shreds of orange
  zest, to decorate

soothing smoothie

Cranberries are a good source of cancer-fighting phytochemicals, and are also soothing for the digestive and urinary tracts. This juice is packed with vitamin C, plus potassium for regulating blood pressure.

Peel the orange, leaving some of the white pith. Juice the orange and cranberries together. Add the peeled banana and yogurt, then blend until smooth. Pour into a glass, sprinkle with shreds of orange zest and serve.

serves 1–2

200 g/7 oz pink forced
  rhubarb
1 orange
2-cm/³/₄-inch piece fresh
  ginger
50 ml/2 fl oz soya milk
pinch of ground ginger,
  to decorate

pink ginger shake

A delicate pink juice that has valuable phytochemicals to boost the immune system and help repair tissues after injury. It's also good for regulating female hormones, and ginger can soothe digestive upsets.

Trim the rhubarb and cut into chunks. Peel the orange, leaving some of the white pith. Juice the rhubarb, orange and ginger. Add the milk and shake or whisk to mix. Pour into a glass, sprinkle with ginger and serve.

serves 1–2

1 apple
1 large carrot
1 celery stick
$^1/_2$ fennel bulb
$^1/_2$ tsp linseeds (flax seeds)

one for the girls

This super juice promotes female hormone balance and is a great treatment for pmt. It also has a calming effect on digestion, and is good for reducing bloating and flatulence.

Juice the apple, carrot, celery and fennel together. Pour into a glass and sprinkle with linseeds to serve.